The Wildlife of

INCHCOLM

(A Comprehensive record of the Birds, Mammals and Plants,
associated with this picturesque Island in the Firth of Forth)

By
Ron Morris

Published by
Hillside
Scotland

Published in Scotland in 2003
by Hillside

ISBN 0-9544760-1-8

Printed in Scotland by
David Macdonald Limited,
25 Rodney Street,
Edinburgh

Hillside
Hillside, Haughgate Street, Leven, Fife, Scotland, U.K. KY8 4SF

INTRODUCTION

Inchcolm lies in the Firth of Forth, about two miles south - west of Aberdour, Fife and about two-thirds of a mile south of Charles Hill Point, across the channel known as Mortimer's Deep.

The island is comprised of two segments (eastern and western), which are linked by a narrow isthmus, at one time covered by the incoming tide, but which has long been built up to form a permanent causeway.

Inchcolm is approximately half a mile long, and covers an area of about twenty-three acres. The eastern portion of the island is hilly, rising to about 100', whilst the larger western part is somewhat flatter, but rises to a similar height at its western extremity, where some stretches of cliffs are to be found.

This very picturesque island is famous for its ancient Abbey and old military fortifications. It has some small, attractive, sandy beaches, but otherwise the coastline is rocky. The surface of the island is well vegetated and there are well kept gardens within the grounds of the Abbey and in the vicinity of the Information Centre.

It is only in fairly recent times that Inchcolm has developed into an important nature reserve for breeding seabird species such as northern fulmar, common eider duck, herring gull, and lesser black-backed gull. The island also has small populations of atlantic puffin, razorbill, black-legged kittiwake and european shag. In previous years, several species of tern bred at the island. Small numbers of grey seal drop their pups at the island's shores each autumn and the common seal has also been known to use the island for pupping during the summer months.

Inchcolm has received very little attention from naturalists in the past and it is hoped that this booklet will not only give the visitor a valuable insight into the island's wealth of natural history, but also provide a sound foundation for any future studies that may take place. I have taken the liberty of including the nearby, small, barren rocks of Carr Craig and Haystack, both of which have been important breeding grounds for several species of tern in the past and in more recent times have hosted important colonies of great cormorant and european shag.

Carr Craig lies less than half a mile north-east of Inchcolm, whilst Haystack lies about the same distance to the west of the island.

ACKNOWLEDGEMENTS

In compiling this booklet, I feel indebted to a number of people who have provided me with valuable assistance and advice necessary for its production and to many others who have supported me over the years during my many visits to Inchcolm. Amongst those who have rendered special assistance are, the late Bob Smith, Betty Smith, Bill Bruce, Murray Wilson, Allan Murray, Mike Ramage, Brian and Stephanie Little, Ron Selley, Derry Dunnet, Hunter Brown, Douglas MacKean, George Ballantyne, and Fife Nature.

Grateful thanks are also due to Bill Simpson (loyal boatman), Colin Aston ("Maid of the Forth"), and Aberdour Boat Club, without whose kindnesses and willingness to assist, much of the information contained herein would never have been gathered, and to Jo Ballingall for carrying out the necessary proof-reading of the manuscript.

I must also extend appreciation to Historic Scotland, owners of Inchcolm, for granting me permission to visit the island for the purpose of investigating its wildlife.

In view of the number of people that I have been in contact with over the years in connection with this project, it is inevitable that I will have overlooked some very deserving individuals, and I take this opportunity to apologize for these oversights.

VISITING INCHCOLM

The "Maid of the Forth" passenger vessel makes regular public sailings from South Queensferry to Inchcolm, between the months of April - October. The vessel is owned by Colin Aston. Enquiries and bookings can be made by contacting the following telephone number

Bookings:- 0131 - 331 - 4857

Bill Simpson, owner of the "Sea Hunter," will also convey visitors to the island from a number of ports in the inner Forth, by individual arrangement. He can be contacted on telehone numbers :-

Home :- 0131 - 538 - 9408

Mobile :- 07774 - 103 - 405

Inchcolm is equipped with toilet facilities which cater for the disabled. It also has a visitor centre and a shop.

CONTENTS

Page

BIRDLIFE

Inchcolm's birdlife has been divided into two sections; "Breeding Birds - Past and Present" and "Non-breeding Birds Recorded from Inchcolm." Thirty-six species are referred to in the first section and forty-six species in the second section.

To qualify for inclusion in the breeding birds'section, a bird species must have at some time in the past been confirmed as having nested, or attempted to nest, at Inchcolm, Carr Craig, or Haystack. Evidence of nesting, or attempted nesting is normally established by way of an empty nest, or a nest containing eggs or young, having been found, or by the presence of recently fledged chicks. Otherwise, a species recorded from any of the three locations mentioned, appears in the non-breeding birds'section.

The following references have been used in compiling both the birdlife sections.

Sibbald; Sir R., Doctor of Medicine, (1710) - History of Fife and Kinross
Forth Seabird Group, (1994-2002) - Annual Forth Island Bird Reports
Rintoul; L.J. & Baxter, E.V. (1935) - a Vertebrate Fauna of Forth
Morris; R.A. (1988-2002) - Brief notes from Breeding Seabird Counts and other records
Ramage; M.- Brief notes on Inchcolm's Birdlife (supplementing R.A. Morris's notes).
Sandeman; G.L. - Brief notes from several visits during the 1940's - 1950's.
Smith; R.W.J. (1959-1995) - Brief notes from breeding seabird counts and other records.

Baxter and Rintoul did not record any seafaring bird species as breeding at Inchcolm in Vertebrate Fauna of Forth (1935), but Carr Craig was noted as a favourite nesting place for sandwich, roseate, and common terns.

Sandeman made a small number of visits to Inchcolm, Carr Craig, and Haystack, during the late 1940's and 1950's, from which he compiled some brief notes which gives us an insight into the colonization of Inchcolm round about that period by species such as northern fulmar, herring gull, lesser black-backed gull, sandwich tern, roseate tern, common tern, and common eider duck, as well as providing us with much of the early information about many of the other breeding, and non-breeding birds on these islands.

Bob Smith began monitoring the breeding seabirds on the islands in the Firth of Forth in 1959. This took the form of a single visit to most of the islands during the peak of the breeding season and has continued every year since, having been carried out in latter years by the Forth Seabird Group, which was founded in 1994, largely on account of Smith's long years of work on the islands. This brief but regular monitoring has proved invaluable in mapping out the colonization of the islands by certain seabird species, as well as recording the population trends of the seabirds breeding in the Firth of Forth as a whole.

Since the late 1980's, R.A.Morris, a member of the Forth Seabird Group, has made a number of visits each year to Inchcolm, Carr Craig, and Haystack, for the purpose of recording ornithological and mammalian data. Most of the information which appears for this period, results from these visits.

As a result of recent changes made by the British Ornithologist's Union's Records Committee, to the common names of many of our bird species for the purpose of standardization, it was considered prudent to adopt the relevant changes and incorporate them into this booklet. Although many people will be unfamiliar with some of these new names, in most cases the character of the changes is unlikely to cause any great confusion.

Hopefully the following pages will go some way to underlining the importance of Inchcolm, Carr Craig, and Haystack, as important wildlife sanctuaries.

ATLANTIC PUFFIN

List of breeding birds - Past & Present

Northern Fulmar
Great Cormorant
European Shag
Mallard
Common Eider
Common Shelduck
Eurasian Oyster Catcher
Common Redshank
Great Black-backed Gull
Lesser Black-backed Gull
Herring Gull
Black-legged Kittiwake
Sandwich Tern
Roseate Tern
Common Tern
Razorbill
Atlantic Puffin
Rock Pigeon / Feral Pigeon
Common Wood Pigeon
Sky Lark
Barn Swallow
Meadow Pipit
Rock Pipit
Pied Wagtail
Winter Wren
Hedge Accentor
European Robin
Common Blackbird
Song Thrush
Eurasian Jackdaw
Carrion Crow
Common Starling
House Sparrow
Chaffinch
Common Linnet
Reed Bunting

BLACK-LEGGED KITTIWAKE

EUROPEAN SHAG

HISTORICAL DETAILS OF INCHCOLM'S BREEDING BIRDS

NORTHERN FULMAR   *Fulmarus glacialis*

The northern fulmar was first recorded from Inchcolm on 13th July 1954 when a single bird was noted. In 1959 two pairs occupied potential nest sites and from then their numbers built up slowly over the years to nine pairs in 1976.

The following year saw a dramatic rise in numbers when there were forty-nine apparently occupied nest sites. Numbers continued to increase over the ensuing years, and reached 256 sites in 1997, before dropping to 149 sites in 1999. However, a new peak of 257 sites was reached in 2000, before dropping again, to 166 sites in 2002.

Out-with the breeding season northern fulmars spend most of their time well out at sea, but do visit the island occasionally for brief periods. On 10th February 1998, thirty northern fulmars were present at Inchcolm, including a "blue phase" individual. This bird was later regularly seen throughout the breeding season and returned the following year, when it occupied a nesting ledge along with a normal phase bird and may have bred.

The blue phase northern fulmar was recorded again on 18th April 2000, but has not been seen at the island since that date.

A solitary northern fulmar flew about the east end of Inchcolm on 24th September 2002 for a brief period, before leaving. This is the latest record for the northern fulmar's presence at the island during the summer months.

The only record of northern fulmar at Haystack or Carr Craig, is of three-four birds gliding around Haystack on 3rd June 1996, as if prospecting the rock for colonization, but to date have not done so.

GREAT CORMORANT   *Phalacrocorax carbo*

Small numbers of great cormorant have probably visited Inchcolm's shores for many years as they are regularly seen, but usually in very small numbers. Their favourite haunts in the area are the nearby rocks of Carr Craig and Haystack, both of which have hosted large breeding colonies in recent times. To date the great cormorant has yet to nest on Inchcolm itself.

The most significant records for great cormorant at Inchcolm are: six birds on 6th March and 13th November 1996, five on 26th September 1997 and eight ashore at the harbour on 13th May 1998.

Out-with the breeding season the most significant records for Carr Craig and Haystack are: over140 birds at Carr Craig on 10th February 1998, thirty birds at Haystack on same date and over thirty birds at Haystack on 23rd March the same year.

The first record of the great cormorant at Carr Craig is of several dozen birds roosting on 1st June 1960. In 1984 the great cormorant probably bred here for the first time, having deserted Cow and Calves rocks (near Inchmickery) that year in favour of this more sizeable location. Breeding was confirmed at Carr Craig in 1985 when an estimated thirty - thirty-five nests were discovered. The colony thereafter grew in size reaching 220 nests in 1991.

Great cormorants readily form new colonies, often deserting their original location only to return some years later. In 1991 Carr Craig held the only nesting colony of great cormorant within the inner Forth. With 220 nests spread over a relatively small surface area, the colony was outgrowing the rock, perhaps repeating what had occurred at the much smaller Cow and Calves rocks a few years beforehand with a few dozen nesting pairs.

The following year, birds from Carr Craig formed new colonies at Haystack, and Inchkeith, resulting in a considerable drop in the numbers breeding at Carr Craig. Only four pairs attempted to breed at Carr Craig in 1994, all of which failed and only five pairs bred in 1995. No great cormorants bred on Carr Craig in 1996. During these years corresponding increases in numbers occurred at the Haystack and Inchkeith colonies, so the decline in numbers at Carr Craig was due to the redistribution of the colony rather than any untoward reduction in the great cormorant population.

In 1997 Carr Craig was re-colonized by seventy-three nesting pairs. This figure rose to 121 nests in 2000, but dropped to ninety-one in 2002. The re-colonization of Carr Craig was basically a return to the rock by the birds from Haystack.

The first record of the great cormorant occurring at Haystack is of thirty-two mainly immature birds on 10th June 1959. Two pairs were suspected of having bred at Haystack in 1991 and were confirmed as doing so during 1992. The following year forty-four pairs nested and in 1994 an even greater movement of Carr Craig's colony occurred when 133 pairs nested at Haystack.

Following this peak figure numbers declined at Haystack, with only eighteen pairs nesting in 1997. This was the last year that the great cormorant bred at this location.

The colony at Inchkeith is now well established in its own right. Most years the colonies at Carr Craig and Inchkeith total in the region of 200 nesting pairs.

During the breeding seasons of 1994 and 1995 a leucistic (cream coloured) great cormorant was present at the Haystack colony and appeared to have bred during the latter year. Its presence provided quite an attraction for passengers on board the "Maid of the Forth," which passes close to the rock on its journeys to and from Inchcolm.

EUROPEAN SHAG   *Phalacrocorax aristotelis*

As with the great cormorant, the european shag has probably frequented Inchcolm's rocks for a very long time and is more commonly found at the island than its larger relative.

However, the european shag had not been the subject of any records until 1990, when a pair bred on the offshore islet, Swallowcraig and continued to do so for the next three years.

In 1992 the first survey of Inchcolm's breeding seabirds for a number of years took place.

Twenty-one european shag nests, which were located mainly in crevices below rocks were counted. In addition to the Swallowcraig pair, it is likely european shags had been nesting elsewhere on the island for a few years but had gone undetected. It would appear they colonized Inchcolm from Carr Craig due to pressure from the growing colony of great cormorants at that rock together with their own expanding numbers.

However, the winters of 1992 and 1993 were particularly severe for european shags up and down the east coast of Scotland, resulting in a very high mortality rate which had a knock on effect on the numbers of breeding shags during the ensuing years.

Since 1994 only very small numbers of the european shag have nested at Inchcolm and although five pairs bred in 2001, only three pairs did so in 2002.

The european shag was first recorded at Carr Craig in 1955 and the first breeding notification occurred in 1973, when one pair was discovered nesting.

Four pairs bred in 1974 and numbers increased over the years to twenty-nine pairs in 1978. Thereafter the population appears to have leveled out until 1987, when twenty-eight pairs nested. Numbers declined afterwards, probably due to some of the birds moving to Inchcolm, followed by the crisis of the severe winters. Only twelve pairs bred in 1993, and the following year no european shags bred at Carr Craig.

However, four pairs bred in 1995 and numbers have fluctuated at the rock since, with between three and seven pairs breeding each year. During 2002 nine pairs bred.

Two european shags were recorded at Haystack on 31st May 1973 and a pair were found nesting on 1st June 1976. This was followed by four pairs nesting in 1977.

Haystack was only surveyed occasionally during the period 1978 - 92, but usually three pairs of european shag were found nesting. However, during the period 1993 - 95, only one pair were recorded breeding each year. Since then numbers have increased, with four pairs nesting in 2002.

MALLARD   *Anas platyrhynchos*

The first record of mallard is from 31st May 1973, when three - four birds were present. However, mallard have undoubtedly had a much longer association with the island than this. There are many further records of them being present in small numbers up until the present time.

The mallard has probably bred at Inchcolm from at least the early 1970's, and has been confirmed as a breeding bird from the 1980's onwards, as nests and broods of ducklings have been witnessed during most years over this period. Up to five nests / broods have been recorded in any one year.

Mallard may be present at any time of the year, but the more significant sightings include: six drakes and three ducks on 23rd March 1998, seven drakes and two ducks on 11th June 1998 and nine drakes and one duck on 30th March 2000.

COMMON EIDER   *Somateria mollissima*

The writer and traveller, Thomas Pennant, in the account of his "Tour in Scotland in 1772," stated he was informed that the eider bred on Inchcolm in the Firth of Forth. However, Baxter and Rintoul (Vertebrate Fauna of Forth, 1935) stated they had no record of recent breeding from that island.

Three pairs of common eider were present during the spring of 1959 and two nests with hatching eggs were discovered on 10th June that year. This is the first confirmed record of breeding in recent times.

Since then Inchcolm has steadily grown in importance as a sanctuary for nesting common eider. During a Nature Conservancy Council (now Scottish Natural Heritage) survey in 1987, 128 common eider nests were found. A similar survey in 1994 returned a count of 258 nests. No further surveys have been made so far, but the current breeding status of the common eider is believed to be in the region of the 1994 figure.

On 30th April 1996 an estimated 250 - 300 birds were offshore, which was about the start of the nesting season. These birds comprised roughly 50% drakes and 50% ducks. Only one nest was found at Inchcolm on that date.

On 29th April 1997 there were a minimum of 239 birds offshore, comprising roughly 60% drakes and 40% ducks. In addition six incubating ducks were found ashore.

The earliest record for breeding during a season is 18th April 2000, when a nest with three eggs was discovered.

During the winter months very few common eider are found around Inchcolm's shores.

Common eider are reported to have bred at Carr Craig a few years before 1932. Single nests were also found at the rock on 1st August 1947 and 22nd July 1948. These records do not state if the nests had any contents but in view of the dates, it is likely the eggs had hatched and the ducklings left the nests, well before the discovery of the nests.

In 1955 a duck accompanied by a brood of ducklings were seen at Carr Craig. Common eider have likely occasionally nested over the years since.

During the years 1994 - 97, between one and three nests were found each year, with single nests witnessed most years since. In 2001 four nests were found, but only two were recorded in 2002.

On 14th May 1996 twenty drakes and several ducks were close inshore at the rock.

At Haystack, a common eider duck and three ducklings were recorded on 2nd June 1978.

One - two nests were found on at least five occasions over the period 1987-1997 and on 1st June 1991 four - five nests were present.

The last indication of breeding at Haystack is the sighting of a single small duckling close inshore at the rock on 13th June 1999.

COMMON SHELDUCK   *Tadorna tadorna*

Common shelduck probably have a lengthy association with Inchcolm. Normally small numbers are seen paired off in the island's bays during the early spring months, followed by occasional sightings during the nesting months.

Indications are that several pairs breed every year, but their choice of nesting sites, i.e. deep under rocks, makes their numbers difficult to census.

The first record for common shelduck is of fourteen birds on 10th June 1959. The island's custodian at the time stated that about ten pairs was the normal figure.

On 1st June 1960 one pair, plus six other individuals were recorded.

A later custodian reported in 1992, that between ten and twelve pairs frequented the island in spring.

Eight pairs were present in south bay on 21st April 1994 and one - two nests were found each year between 1995 and 1997. Five pairs were recorded on 24th April 1999 and again on 18th April 2000. A nest containing seven eggs was found on 29th May 2001.

Three-four pairs of common shelduck were present on 22nd June 2002.

EURASIAN OYSTER CATCHER   *Haematopus ostralegus*

The first notification of eurasian oyster catcher occurring at Inchcolm is of a single bird on 10th June 1959. One pair was present on each of the dates, 31st May 1973 and 4th June 1974. From that time the numbers of potentially breeding pairs increased slowly to between five and seven pairs during the 1990's, with possibly as much as eight pairs holding territories during 1996.

Nests with eggs have been found since at least the early 1980's. During a survey from 29th - 30th May 2001, eight nests containing eggs were found, the highest figure to date. Twelve pairs appeared to be holding territories during 2002, but it was not established how many actually nested.

Flocks of seventy and thirty birds were recorded on 11th May 1974 and 2nd June 1978, respectively. Andrews reported in "Birds of the Lothians (1986)," that flocks of c.500 birds are known to roost on Inchcolm. However, most visits outwith the breeding season will reveal the eurasian oyster catcher in very small numbers.

Sandeman reported a possible eurasian oyster catcher nest with two eggs at Carr Craig, on 8th July 1947, but as there was a large number of terns nesting then, this potential record was not confirmed.

Ten birds were present at Carr Craig on 24th June 1997. Most years from 1991 onwards, one - two birds have been seen at the rock during the breeding season and in some years a pair have been suspected of holding a breeding territory, but so far breeding has not been established.

Two birds were present at the rock on 25th November 2002.

At Haystack, single birds were recorded on 29th April and 17th June 1997 and on 13th June 1999. A pair was present on 31st May 2002, but do not appear to have bred. Two birds were noted at the rock on 25th November 2002.

COMMON REDSHANK *Tringa totanus*

Six records exist for the common redshank occurring at Inchcolm. Single birds were recorded on 13th July 1954, 19th July 1955 and 31st October 1994, two - three birds were present on 13th November the same year, three birds on 18th April 2000 and two birds on 24th September 2002.

A reliable report exists of a pair of common redshank nesting at Carr Craig some time during the 1930's. At that time the rock was apparently well vegetated. Other than this, there are no other records to date of this species being found at this rock.

Two birds were ashore at Haystack on 13th November 1996.

GREAT BLACK-BACKED GULL *Larus marinus*

The first record of great black-backed gull occurring at Inchcolm is from 19th July 1955, when a single bird was present. There are no further records until 12th June 1994, when an immature bird was noted. Since then small numbers have been recorded each year. Five birds, four adults and one juvenile, were seen on 6th March 1996.

Breeding first took place in 1995, when a nesting pair with a single chick were discovered amongst the herring gull and lesser black-backed gull colonies. A pair has bred at Inchcolm during most years since.

Outside the breeding season small numbers of great black-backed gulls may be seen at the island.

There are four records for Carr Craig: single birds on 19th September 1995 and 8th July 1997, one adult and one immature bird on 10th February 1998 and two birds on 10th November 2001.

Three records exist for Haystack: a second year bird ashore on 29th April 1997, an immature bird on 24th April 1999 and two adults and one immature bird on 25th November 2002.

LESSER BLACK-BACKED GULL *Larus fuscus*

The first record of lesser black-backed gull occurring at Inchcolm is of a single bird on 19th July 1955.

In 1973 a colony of breeding lesser black-backed gulls (presumably small in number) was reported to be at the island's north-west slopes. The following year this colony was estimated at about ten pairs, which increased in size to "dozens" by 1981.

A rapid expansion in the colony size took place during the 1980's and a Nature Conservancy Council survey at the beginning of June 1987, returned an estimate of 730 breeding pairs of lesser black-backed gulls.

The next survey of Inchcolm's large gull populations took place during May 1994 by Scottish Natural Heritage (formerly Nature Conservancy Council), who at that time estimated 1,669 lesser black-backed gull nests.

Since that time lesser black-backed gull numbers appear to have stabilized at the island, although to date no further survey has been carried out.

The lesser black-backed gull is largely a migratory species leaving the island during late August - September and returning during March.

One pair of lesser black-backed gulls were found tending a nest containing three one day old chicks on 13th May 1998, which is a very advanced stage in the breeding season for this species. Many other lesser black-backed gulls had only recently laid their eggs and a good number of others hadn't even started building their nests by that time.

On 24th September 2002 there were still two - three adult lesser black-backed gulls at Inchcolm, one of which had two fledged juveniles accompanying it.

Two lesser black-backed gulls were present at Carr Craig on 31st May 1973 and on 24th June 1977 two nests were recorded from the rock. The lesser black-backed gull has probably continued nesting at Carr Craig, on and off, since that time.

One - two pairs nested during 1994 and between the years 1995 –2000 two - three pairs bred. They may have bred during 2001, however there were no obvious signs of them nesting during 2002.

Single pairs of lesser black-backed gull nested at Haystack during the years 1992 and 1996. Four birds were present on 27th May 1997 and two on 31st May 2002 but their breeding status was not confirmed.

HERRING GULL   *Larus argentatus*

Most likely the herring gull has always visited Inchcolm. At least one pair bred in 1950 at the jetty, alongside several pairs of common terns.

A pair may have attempted to breed in 1960, but the next definite notification we have is from 31st May 1973 when the herring gull is described as "numerous and breeding." In 1974 it was estimated that between 250 - 300 pairs were nesting.

Numbers increased over the following years and a Nature Conservancy Council survey on 2nd June 1987 returned 1,040 nesting pairs at the island When Scottish Natural Heritage (formerly Nature Conservancy Council) repeated the survey in 1994, it was estimated there were 1,615 herring gull nests.

The herring gull usually begins returning to Inchcolm during February or March for the breeding season and leaves again by September. Out-with the breeding season, the herring gull's presence at Inchcolm can vary from very few birds to a few hundred. On 13th November 1996 about 200 adult and immature birds were present and c.150 birds were recorded on 10th November 2001. Thirty - forty, birds were seen at the island on 24th September 2002, but on 25th November the same year, only five birds were noted, all flying over the island.

On 31st July 1948 two herring gull chicks, close to fledging, were discovered at Carr Craig. When the rock was visited on 4th July 1951 thirty - forty pairs of herring gull were found nesting. During this visit it was noticed that all the vegetation had been worn away from Carr Craig, making the rock look as if it had been completely fouled or burned in comparison with former years. In 1955, Carr Craig was described as a stinking mess of dung and had been completely taken over by herring gulls, with probably 100 - 200 pairs nesting.

The herring gull was reported as "breeding numerously" at Carr Craig in 1959 and was apparently the only species present at the rock.

On 2nd June 1978 c.112 nests were counted, but on 1st June 1987 only twenty-eight nests were found. It is likely most of the colony had shifted to Inchcolm under pressure from the expanding colony of great cormorants which had colonized Carr Craig a few years beforehand.

Surveys of herring gull numbers at Carr Craig have taken place almost every year since, with the colony varying between thirty-eight and sixty nesting pairs. There were forty-eight nests in 2002.

The herring gull was described as "probably breeding" at Haystack on 10th June 1959. During May 1973 there were approximately forty-five - fifty pairs nesting and in 1975 this figure had risen to about eighty pairs. Numbers remained high until about the early 1980's but in 1987 only twenty-two nests were found. Since 1993 the colony has been monitored annually and has varied in size between eleven - twenty-two breeding pairs. There were eighteen nests on 31st May 2002.

BLACK-LEGGED KITTIWAKE   *Rissa tridactyla*

A single black-legged kittiwake was recorded from Inchcolm on 13th July 1954 and on 10th June 1959 a party of this species was seen close to the island. The next record is of three or four birds flying past the island on 31st May 1973.

The black-legged kittiwake apparently began to frequent Inchcolm more often during the late 1980's. Breeding was first recorded during 1991, when about twenty pairs were discovered nesting at the north-west cliffs. It is possible breeding actually began at this location the previous year.

Numbers built up at the colony over the following years, reaching a peak of 190 nests in 1995, but afterwards the breeding population started to decline, with only forty-two pairs nesting in 2001. However, this figure increased to fifty-eight nesting pairs in 2002.

A party of six black-legged kittiwakes were recorded flying past Carr Craig on 3rd June 1996.

SANDWICH TERN   *Sterna sandvicensis*

During 1954 a colony of about 100 pairs of sandwich terns attempted to nest at Inchcolm. However, a visit to the colony on 13th July revealed only five or six adult birds present, along with many broken, sucked, or deserted eggs. The cause of this misfortune was not ascertained.

It is unknown if sandwich terns had attempted to nest at Inchcolm prior to 1954, but they were not recorded during a visit in July 1955.

On 10th June 1959 sandwich terns were seen flying in the vicinity of the island, but they were not recorded again until 23rd June 1976 when four birds were seen flying by.

Small numbers have been recorded fairly regularly during the summer months from 1994 to the present time. Usually these birds are merely flying by Inchcolm or feeding in its bays. Ten birds were noted on 19th September 1995 and six on 24th September 2002.

Sandwich terns appear to have nested on Carr Craig over the decades leading up to 1950.

Baxter and Rintoul (Vertebrate Fauna of Forth, 1935) stated that "sandwich terns nested on Carr Craig," but, although they do not qualify this statement with a period of time, it does suggest the species was established at the rock.

A visit to Carr Craig on 8th July 1947 found between fifteen - twenty pairs nesting. This number rose to between twenty - thirty by 1st August that year. The following year it was estimated there were between 150 - 250 breeding pairs. Over 176 chicks were ringed that year, accompanied by the claim that double that number could have been ringed, which suggests the upper level of that estimate is the more accurate.

In July 1950 tern numbers (all species) at Carr Craig are described as being many fewer than in previous years, but a good, thick, white carpet of sandwich terns was reported. However, in 1951 no tern species nested at the rock. It was noticed that the surface of Carr Craig had been transformed into bare rock, having had all its vegetation worn away. These circumstances appear to have arisen as a result of the herring gull becoming established at the rock and, through its nesting and dunging habits, destroyed the vegetation and, competing in growing numbers with the terns for nesting space, they ultimately drove the terns away from Carr Craig.

The next notification we have of sandwich terns occurring at Carr Craig is of four birds flying over the rock on 25th May 1994. Carr Craig still remains virtually devoid of any vegetation and, the prospect of sandwich terns ever returning to this rock to breed will remain bleak until the herring gull colony declines and vegetation is restored.

The only record of sandwich terns at Haystack is of two birds flying over the rock on 13th June 1999.

ROSEATE TERN   *Sterna dougallii*

The roseate tern apparently re-colonized the Forth estuary in 1931, with there being about 250 pairs nesting, mainly on Carr Craig.

On 8th July 1947 there were an estimated thirty - fifty pairs nesting at Carr Craig, but a further visit on 1st August that year revealed numbers had risen to about 100 pairs. In July the following year about 250 pairs nested and 254 chicks were ringed.

In July 1950, "terns"(i.e. common, roseate, and sandwich terns) were reported to be far fewer in number than during previous years and in 1951 all three species of tern which had formerly nested at the rock, had deserted it.

The only record of terns nesting at Carr Craig since then is of four pairs in 1969. Unfortunately the exact species were not identified.

Many of Carr Craig's roseate terns moved to Inchgarvie where they nested between the years 1951-53. Afterwards the colony moved to Inchmickery where they returned every year, in ever decreasing numbers, until a few years ago when they ceased to do so. Only a very small number of roseate terns now return to the Forth estuary each year to breed.

In 1954 about twenty pairs of roseate terns bred at Inchcolm and between one - ten pairs nested in 1969. A few pairs also bred in 1971.

The only record of roseate terns at Inchcolm since 1971 is of two birds which were resting on a dinghy in the harbour, on 13th June 1999. There are no records for Carr Craig since 1950.

COMMON TERN   *Sterna hirundo*

Baxter and Rintoul (Vertebrate Fauna of Forth, 1935) stated that Carr Craig is a breeding place of this species, along with Inchmickery. They also stated that, "terns bred in considerable numbers in the Forth area in old days. Then some species disappeared altogether and others became very scarce as breeding birds. In recent years they have returned and breed in all their former abundance."

On 8th July 1947 Sandeman recorded between 200-300 pairs of common terns nesting on Carr Craig. The following year he reported them as being present in "fair numbers", but in July 1950 they were considerably fewer than in previous years and, like the roseate and sandwich terns, deserted the rock after that time.

Although four pairs of terns nested at Carr Craig in 1969 the actual species was not established.

The next record of common terns at Carr Craig is of two birds on 26th June 1995 calling to each other as they flew over the rock.

Common terns were noted as being present on Swallowcraig, the small rocky islet at Inchcolm's harbour, on 24th July 1948. In 1950 common or arctic terns (most probably common terns) were reported to be nesting at Swallowcraig, whilst two-three pairs of common terns also nested at the jetty. Some common terns were present at Inchcolm in July 1954 and are said to have attempted to breed, whilst some were present on Swallowcraig on 19th July 1955.

During 1959 about twelve pairs of common or arctic terns (again likely to be common terns) were reported to have nested at Swallowcraig.

In 1969 between ten and one hundred pairs of common terns nested at Inchcolm. During 1973 six or seven pairs bred. The following two years a small number of birds were present and may have bred, but this was not confirmed. On 23rd June 1976 a pair of common terns were seen flying about carrying fish, which suggests they may have been feeding chicks at the island. At least two birds were present on 2nd June 1978.

Since these times no breeding has taken place at Inchcolm. However, during the summer months, small numbers of common terns are occasionally recorded flying in the vicinity of Inchcolm or feeding in its bays. The most significant records are of nine birds on 14th May 1996 and seven on 13th June 1999. Two birds flew past the island on 3rd June 2002.

Sandeman recorded a "good colony" of common terns nesting at Haystack on 4th July 1951, which was obviously part of the colony formerly at Carr Craig. It appears these common terns moved to Inchmickery soon afterwards. A single common tern was seen flying over Haystack on 13th June 1999.

RAZORBILL   *Alca torda*

The razorbill is first notified from Inchcolm on 1st June 1993, when a group of twenty - twenty-five birds were seen offshore.

During the breeding season of 1994, two - four razorbills frequented the cliffs at the north - west of the island and on 19th July that year, eight birds were recorded offshore. Two pairs were discovered breeding the following year and on 17th June twenty - twenty-two birds were recorded in the vicinity of the island.

Razorbills have continued to be present in small numbers during the summer months. Between two - four pairs bred at the island each year over the period 1996 - 99. However, eleven nest sites were counted in 2000, at least five during 2001 and at least eleven again in 2002.

On 24th September 2002 six razorbills were close inshore at Inchcolm.

ATLANTIC PUFFIN   *Fratercula arctica*

From the late 1980's up until 1991, small numbers of atlantic puffin were seen frequenting the waters around Inchcolm during the breeding season, but no birds were seen ashore.

On 14th June 1992 about fifty birds were observed on the sea, close to the island and some burrowing attempts, possibly by atlantic puffins, were discovered at the island's north-west point.

A puffin egg was found in a rock cavity at Inchcolm's south-east corner on 1st June 1993, with at least three other nesting sites discovered deep under the rocks. Sixty birds were counted on and offshore on 18th June.

Breeding has taken place at the island each year since and is normally confirmed by observing adult birds carrying small fish in their bills to feed their chicks.

The puffin colony originally established itself at the south side of Inchcolm's eastern part, but some birds spread to the slopes at the north-west of the island and after a few years, the whole colony re-located to this point.

The size of the colony is likely to be no more than two or three dozen pairs, but actual breeding numbers are difficult to assess due to the puffin's habit of nesting down burrows or under rocks.

On 26th June 1995 eighty-nine birds were counted on and offshore, likewise seventy birds on 15th June 1996 and eighty birds on 8th July 1997. However, during some R.S.P.B. Puffin Cruises over this period, in excess of 100 birds were occasionally seen. Many of these birds would have been non-breeding birds.

The presence of the black rat on Inchcolm may be a factor in limiting the atlantic puffin's increase, as rats usually cause havoc whenever they occur at puffin colonies. They may also be the reason for the colony shifting from the boulder slopes where they originally bred, to the less accessible cliffs at the island's west end.

Fifty-eight birds were counted, on and offshore, on 3rd June 2002.

Two birds were seen close inshore at Carr Craig on 14th May 1996 and fifteen birds were close inshore at Haystack on 8th July 1997.

ROCK PIGEON / FERAL PIGEON   *Columba livia*

The rock pigeon's association with Inchcolm probably goes back to at least the 13th century when the tower was added to the Abbey. The tower doubled as a dovecot, as the inside of its walls were prepared with nesting chambers for rock pigeons, which provided a source of food for the monks at the Abbey.

Dr. Sibbald in his "History of Fife and Kinross" (1710), stated, "a great many pigeons and crowes nest in the ruins of the monastery, and in the rocks".

Because the true strain of the rock pigeon has been corrupted through inter-breeding with domestic strains of pigeon, producing a wide variety of unnatural coloration in the species, it is largely ignored by serious birdwatchers and naturalists.

Over thirty rock/feral pigeons were recorded at Inchcolm on 23rd June 1976, although this could easily have been a large understatement of the true population. On 14th June 1992 the island's population was noted as "hundreds". About 500 birds were recorded on 13th November 1996 and, at least one pair were still feeding squabs in the nest on that date.

The rock pigeon has continued to be present in high numbers at Inchcolm.

Two birds were present at Carr Craig on 25th May 1994 and 13th June 1999 and single birds were recorded on 30th May 2000 and 30th May 2001.

The rock pigeon was suspected to be nesting in a "blow hole" fissure at Haystack on 6th July 1993. It was first "confirmed" as breeding at this rock on 24th May 1997 when a bird was flushed from a nest containing two eggs. Breeding was also suspected during May 2000 and May 2002.

Usually one - two rock pigeons are seen at this rock during a visit.

COMMON WOOD PIGEON   *Columba palumbus*

An old nest of the common wood pigeon was discovered at Inchcolm on 10th June 1959. However, the first record of a bird was of an individual on 23rd June 1976. One pair was present on 2nd June 1987 and a single bird was again recorded on 21st August 1993.

At least three pairs bred in 1994 and the following year, seven pairs were discovered nesting.

In 1997 an incubating bird was discovered on 24th May, seven further occupied nests were found on 17th June and a further occupied nest along with two "new" but empty nests, were found on 8th July.

Breeding has been proved every year since though no proper census has been carried out. On 27th July 1999 a common wood pigeon was found incubating four eggs, rather than the usual clutch of two and a bird was discovered incubating eggs on 24th September 2002.

Most common wood pigeon nests are located in the many elder bushes which are spread over the island. The breeding population at Inchcolm will vary from year to year, but in most years there will be a minimum of two or three pairs nesting, with perhaps up to ten or a dozen pairs. Few birds are actually seen about the island during the nesting season, which indicates the common wood pigeon seeks most of its food on the mainland.

SKY LARK   *Alauda arvensis*

Sandeman recorded the sky lark on three occasions: one bird on 24th July 1948, five - six birds on 15th July 1950 and one - two birds on 13th July 1954. On 10th June 1959 one or two birds were observed singing and on 2nd June 1978 three birds were seen, two of which were also heard singing.

During the early - mid 1980's small numbers of sky larks were present at the island during the nesting season, and were heard singing.

Although the sky lark has not been confirmed as a breeding bird by the normal criteria, the aforementioned observations for this species suggest that breeding took place.

This species has been in decline on a national basis in recent years and its long grass habitat at Inchcolm has been completely taken over by gulls during the nesting season.

BARN SWALLOW   *Hirundo rustica*

The first record of barn swallow at Inchcolm is of a single bird on 13th July 1954. In 1958 a pair of barn swallows bred and raised four young and there was possibly a pair present in 1959. Three birds were witnessed on 1st June 1960 and breeding may have taken place that year.

From at least 1974 until 1991 a pair of barn swallows nested each year, and in 1987 two pairs bred. In 1992 the island's custodian reported that no swallows had returned that year, breaking a long sequence of annual visits.

Between the years 1994 - 97, one - three birds were noted during a number of summer visits.

Fifteen barn swallows were recorded flying south to north over the island, in one's and two's, on 13th May 1998.

During 1999 a pair attempted to breed, building a nest in the monks' dormitory within the Abbey, but it appears they were unsuccessful.

A single bird was recorded on 18th April 2000 and two were present on 30th May 2001.

The barn swallow was not recorded during the breeding season of 2002, but on 24th September twenty-one birds were recorded flying westwards over the island in small parties.

MEADOW PIPIT   *Anthus pratensis*

A meadow pipit was seen carrying food at Inchcolm on 15th July 1950 and the species is recorded as possibly being present on 13th July 1954 and 10th June 1959.

The meadow pipit was seen occasionally during the summer months of the early - mid 1980's.

Like the sky lark, the meadow pipit has probably bred in the past (the record from 1950 suggests this to be the case), but its habitat has now been taken over by gulls during the nesting season.

Two birds were recorded on 10th April 1997 and at least two were present on 24th September and 25th November 2002.

ROCK PIPIT   *Anthus petrosus*

Baxter and Rintoul (Vertebrate Fauna of Forth, 1935) stated that rock pipits nest on Inchcolm and Carr Craig. Sandeman recorded individuals present at the latter location on 8th July 1947 and 22nd July 1948. On 24th July 1948 he reported "good numbers" were present on Inchcolm. He also recorded their presence at Inchcolm on 13th July 1954 and 19th July 1955, on the latter date as "carrying food".

Several individual rock pipits were recorded at Inchcolm on 10th June 1959 and several pairs were noted on 1st June the following year.

The rock pipit has not been recorded at Inchcolm or Carr Craig during the breeding season since those times, but there are six records of them being present during the spring and autumn months at Inchcolm: two birds on 21st April and 31st October

1994 and 6th March 1996, at least six birds on 13th November 1996, several on 10th November 2001 and four - five present on 25th November 2002.

PIED WAGTAIL *Motacilla alba*

The pied wagtail was first recorded from Inchcolm on 29th July 1948. It bred during at least three years from the mid - late 1950's, but was no longer present in 1959.

A fledged brood of pied wagtails were recorded in 1975 and single birds were occasionally recorded over the following years. One pair was seen flying with young on 2nd June 1987 and the species has probably nested during most years since.

Another pair of pied wagtails was recorded feeding three fledged young on 28th June 1994 and, on the same date, a nest was discovered high up in a vaulted room within the Abbey. Further breeding was confirmed in 1995, 1997, 1998 and 2002. Five birds were recorded on 24th September 2002.

WINTER WREN *Troglodytes troglodytes*

The winter wren was reported to be breeding on Inchcolm in 1987, but this species undoubtedly has a much longer association with the island.

Individual birds were seen in April and June 1994 and a family of at least seven birds was seen in some bushes. Most of these birds were recent fledglings.

One - three pairs have been confirmed breeding during most years since, usually building their domed nests in the vicinity of the Abbey and its gardens.

The autumn and winter months bring an influx of winter wrens to Inchcolm's shores. Eleven birds were counted on 31st October 1994, more than fourteen on 6th March 1996, ten - twelve birds on 10th February 1998 and "many" were present on 25th November 2002.

HEDGE ACCENTOR *Prunella modularis*

The hedge accentor, or dunnock, was first recorded at Inchcolm on 23rd June 1976, when a single bird was noted. However, the island's custodian reported this species as nesting in 1992 and it is likely the hedge accentor had done so at various other times over the years.

From 1994 onwards one - two hedge accentors have been recorded each year during the breeding season and it is probable that it still occasionally breeds.

Out-with the breeding season, small numbers are usually present at the island. At least four birds were seen on 13th November 1996, another one on 10th November 2001 and at least three on 25th November 2002.

EUROPEAN ROBIN *Erithacus rubecula*

An immature european robin was recorded on Inchcolm on 15th July 1950 and in 1987 the species was described as a winter visitor to the island.

On 15th June 1996, two birds were noted, one of which was regularly seen carrying food to a possible nest site. On 27th May the following year, another bird was also seen carrying food. Two pairs were recorded and probably bred during 1998. A nest was found on 13th May that year containing two broken eggshells, but the condition of the nest suggested it may have been from the previous year. One bird was seen carrying food on 11th June. Up to three individuals have been seen during each breeding season since.

Out-with the breeding season over fifteen birds were recorded on 13th November 1996 and "many" were present on 24th September and 25th November 2002.

COMMON BLACKBIRD   *Turdus merula*

Single male common blackbirds were noted at Inchcolm on 24th and 29th July 1948. Two - three birds were seen on 15th July 1950 along with a nest.

On 13th July 1954 four - five birds were present. Several were recorded in June 1959 and on 1st June the following year, a minimum of six were noted.

At least one pair bred in 1978. Breeding was also confirmed in 1987 and 1992.

Since 1994 small numbers have been recorded regularly during the breeding season, with breeding proved during most years and up to three pairs nesting in any one year. At least fifteen birds were present on 25th November 2002.

SONG THRUSH   *Turdus philomelos*

At least one bird, which was singing, was present at Inchcolm on 10th June 1959. Another bird, and perhaps more, was recorded on 1st June 1960. The next record is of an individual on 23rd June 1976.

In June 1987 the island's custodian reported the song thrush as breeding at Inchcolm.

The song thrush was not recorded again until 25th November 2002 when at least two birds were present.

EURASIAN JACKDAW   *Corvus monedula*

Dr. Sibbald in his "History of Fife and Kinross" (1710) stated, "a great many pigeons and crowes nest in the ruins of the monastery, and in the rocks". The "crowes" he was referring to, were almost certainly eurasian jackdaws, judging by his description of their nest sites.

Furthermore, Dickson (Emeralds Chased in Gold, 1899) stated, "jackdaws sometimes haunt the ruins". However, Baxter and Rintoul did not make any mention of the eurasian jackdaw occurring at Inchcolm in their time, i.e. early-mid 20th century.

Two birds were recorded at Inchcolm on 23rd June 1976 and two were again noted during the same month in 1978. On 2nd June 1987 two pairs were described as "probably breeding".

Between 1992 - 2001 it was estimated there was a colony of between twenty - twenty-four birds spread over the island during the breeding season, nesting in the cliffs, or under rocks. After the breeding season the eurasian jackdaw returns to the mainland.

Only about six - eight birds were seen during the breeding season of 2002. Five birds were recorded on 24th September, that year.

CARRION CROW *Corvus corone*

Two carrion crows were recorded at Inchcolm on 15th July 1950. The next record for the island is of two birds being present on 2nd June 1978.

In 1987 the carrion crow was reported to be breeding at the island and it is likely that at least one pair and sometimes two pairs have bred during most years since. In 1994 two nests were found containing four and five chicks respectively.

Occasionally a pair of carrion crows will attempt to nest on the circular walkway around the lighthouse tower, but the nest is usually removed as a matter of necessity for the maintenance of the light.

Two - three carrion crows were recorded on 24th September and two on 25th November 2002.

One pair of carrion crows was recorded at Carr Craig in 1955. During the years 1994 - 2001 single birds or pairs were regularly recorded from this rock, but up to three had been noted. Most of these records are for the months May - July, but one record exists for February. These birds are usually Inchcolm's crows visiting Carr Craig on feeding trips.

Single birds and sometimes two, were recorded regularly at Haystack during the months April-September over the years 1994 - 2000. These birds were normally seen coming from, or returning to, the Braefoot area of the Fife coastline.

COMMON STARLING *Sturnus vulgaris*

Baxter and Rintoul (Vertebrate Fauna of Forth, 1935) stated that starlings breed on many of the islands in the Forth and that they saw them on Inchcolm in 1929.

About twenty common starlings were recorded at Inchcolm on 15th July 1950. Two were present on 13th July 1954 and between twenty - thirty were noted on 19th July 1955.

On 10th July 1959 it was reported that many common starlings roosted on the island. It was also described as "breeding".

A flock of 100 was recorded on 23rd June 1976 and on 2nd June 1978 adult common starlings, accompanied by juveniles, were seen.

Adult birds feeding fledged juveniles, were witnessed each breeding season between 1993-97 and flocks of between twenty-five - fifty birds were occasionally recorded. In 1995 the island's custodian reported that large numbers gather in the evening.

During 1998 a pair of common starlings bred in the old military engine house at the south-east part of Inchcolm. Small numbers continue to be recorded during each breeding season, with an adult feeding three fledged juveniles being seen on 3rd June 2002. Ten common starlings were present on 24th September 2002.

HOUSE SPARROW *Passer domesticus*

Dickson (Emeralds Chased in Gold, 1899) stated that the "chirp of the sparrow"(house sparrow) may be heard on Inchcolm. In 1922 a Ministry of Works official reported the island was invaded by house sparrows. At that time military personnel and buildings were still on the island following the First World War.

Baxter and Rintoul (Vertebrate Fauna of Forth, 1935) stated the house sparrow nests on the island. Sandeman recorded the house sparrow in July of the years 1948, 1950 and 1954, stating they were common in the latter year. Although they were reported not to breed in 1959, they were present in the area of the custodians's house, near the Abbey, the following year.

Several house sparrows were noted on 23rd June 1976, but since then there have been no records of the sparrow being sighted, nor of its "chirp" being heard, at the island.

CHAFFINCH   *Fringilla coelebs*

A male chaffinch was recorded at Inchcolm on 10th June 1959, and one or two birds were present on 1st June 1960. On 2nd June 1987 chaffinches were reported to be breeding.

Between 1994 - 2002 the chaffinch has been recorded occasionally most years and has bred during at least some of these years.

A male bird was seen carrying food on 1st June 1995, two pairs were recorded on 13th May 1998, with at least one pair carrying food to an undiscovered nest, and one - two pairs were noted over 29th - 30th May 2001, although breeding was not confirmed that year.

Out-with the spring - summer months the chaffinch has been seen at the island during the month of November, the last record being of at least one bird on 24th November 2002.

COMMON LINNET   *Carduelis cannabina*

Sandeman recorded small numbers of the common linnet at Inchcolm during the month of July in the years 1948, 1950,1954 and 1955.

It has been reported many times over the years since 1959, but no more than eight birds have been recorded on any one date, except 24th September 2002 when eleven birds were noted and 25th November 2002 when a flock of at least twenty birds was present.

During the early 1980's, an occasional nest was found and in 1992 the island's custodian reported them as nesting. On 13th May 1998 at least three pairs were present, but breeding was not proved. There are usually one - two pairs present during each breeding season.

REED BUNTING   *Emberiza schoeniclus*

Sandeman recorded a male reed bunting with two - three juveniles at Inchcolm on 13th July 1954. This is the only record of this species from the island.

List of Non - Breeding Birds recorded from Inchcolm

Red-throated Diver
Black-throated Diver
Manx Shearwater
Northern Gannet
Grey Heron
Mute Swan
Greylag Goose
Canada Goose
Eurasian Wigeon
Gadwall
Northern Shoveler
Velvet Scoter
Red-breasted Merganser
Eurasian Sparrowhawk
Common Buzzard
Common Kestrel
Peregrine Falcon
Corn Crake
Common Coot
Ringed Plover
European Golden Plover
Purple Sandpiper
Dunlin
Common Sandpiper
Whimbrel
Eurasian Curlew
Ruddy Turnstone
Pomarine Skua
Arctic Skua
Black-headed Gull

Mew Gull
Common Guillemot
Stock Pigeon
Common Cuckoo
Common Swift
Great Spotted Woodpecker
House Martin
Northern Wheatear
Fieldfare
Redwing
Willow Warbler
Blue Tit
Rook
European Greenfinch
European Bullfinch
Chilean Flamingo

Black-Legged Kittiwake Chicks

Historical Details of Non - Breeding Birds recorded from Inchcolm

RED-THROATED DIVER   *Gavia stellata*

A single bird was sighted close inshore to Carr Craig on 10th November 2001.

BLACK-THROATED DIVER   *Gavia arctica*

A single bird flew past Carr Craig on 8th June 2002.

MANX SHEARWATER   *Puffinus puffinus*

Seven manx shearwaters were recorded near Inchcolm on 10th June 1959.

NORTHERN GANNET   *Morus bassanus*

An injured or ill, adult bird was ashore at the south-west bay on 1st May 1995 and was found dead on 4th May at the same location.

On 30th April 1996 a party of twelve birds flew eastwards off the north side of the island, and on 15th June the same year, a party of fifteen birds were also seen flying eastwards off the north side of the island.

Thirty-five northern gannets were feeding off the north side of the Inchcolm on 13th June 1999 and, on 30th May 2001, about thirty northern gannets were observed flying west off the island's north side.

On 3rd June 1999 a party of eight birds were recorded flying past Carr Craig.

GREY HERON   *Ardea cinerea*

A single bird was ashore on 26th September 1997. Individuals were also present on 23rd March and 26th May 1998. Two grey herons were present on 24th September 2002.

MUTE SWAN   *Cygnus olor*

A juvenile bird visited the island's north bay on 30th April 1999. During late April-early May 2002 a pair of mute swans visited Inchcolm for two - three days. One of the birds went through the ritual of assembling some nesting material in north bay. It is believed this was the same pair of swans which frequent Port Edgar.

GREYLAG GOOSE   *Anser anser*

The greylag goose has been recorded at Inchcolm several times in recent years.

Two birds were ashore on 3rd June 1994, as were another two, on or about 25th April 1995. Single birds were recorded on 6th March 1996 and 17th June 1997 (close inshore).

A flock of about fifty greylag geese flew northwards in V-formation over the island on 30th April 1996.

A single bird was present at the west end of the island on 10th February 1998 and, on the same day, twenty-seven "grey geese" flew overhead from south-west to north-east.

Fourteen greylags also flew over the island, from south to north, on 15th June 1999 and a pair settled in south bay on 29th May 2001.

ATLANTIC PUFFINS

COMMON EIDER DUCKLINGS HATCHING

NORTHERN FULMAR

EURASIAN OYSTER CATCHER

GREY SEAL PUP

COMMON SEALS

TREE MALLOW

LESSER CELANDINE

CANADA GOOSE   *Branta canadensis*

A solitary canada goose arrived at Inchcolm during late June 2002 and remained at the island until about mid-September. It fed and roosted within the grounds of the Abbey. This bird was ringed, but the details were not obtained.

EURASIAN WIGEON   *Anas penelope*

The eurasian wigeon has been recorded twice at Inchcolm so far. A drake was in south bay on 13th November 1996 and a pair were at the same location, on 11th June 1998.

GADWALL   *Anas strepera*

Six gadwall were ashore at the west point of Inchcolm's north bay, on 15th June 1996.

NORTHERN SHOVELER   *Anas clypeata*

A pair of shoveler flew around Inchcolm's south-west bay on 24th April 1999.

VELVET SCOTER   *Melanitta fusca*

On 25th May 1994 a flock of between eighteen - twenty birds was seen flying eastwards off the north side of the island.

RED-BREASTED MERGANSER   *Mergus serrator*

There are four records of red-breasted merganser occurring at Inchcolm: one pair flying over the island on 21st April 1994, one drake and three ducks present on 6th March 1996, three ducks present on 13th November the same year and a pair close inshore on 10th February 1998.

There are also two records for Carr Craig. Four birds were seen close inshore on 10th February 1998, as was a solitary drake on 25th November 2002.

EURASIAN SPARROWHAWK   *Accipiter nisus*

The remains of bird of prey kills, usually feral pigeons, are commonly found on Inchcolm and are the work of visiting eurasian sparrowhawks and peregrine falcons.

A female eurasian sparrowhawk over-wintered on the island during 1985 - 86 and again in1986 - 87. Other individual birds were recorded on 21st April and 31st October 1994, 6th March and 13th November 1996, 23rd March 1998 and 24th September 2002.

COMMON BUZZARD   *Buteo buteo*

A common buzzard visited the west side of Inchcolm on 25th November 2002.

COMMON KESTREL   *Falco tinnunculus*

Common kestrels are known to have occasionally visited Inchcolm during the summer months of the early - mid 1980's. These birds were seen coming from the Fife mainland. On 24th September 2002 a male bird was observed hovering over the island's west side.

PEREGRINE FALCON   *Falco peregrinus*

This species appears to be an increasing visitor to Inchcolm. On 4th May 1995 a peregrine falcon was seen diving unsuccessfully, at seabirds over south bay and, on 26th June the same year, a peregrine was again recorded.

On 26th May 1998 a peregrine was witnessed killing a species of gull at the island's west end.

A pair of peregrines was present at the cliffs at the island's west end on 10th November 2001, where they were heard calling to one another. The remains of several feral pigeons and a eurasian curlew (peregrine kills) were also found.

On 6th July 2002 a peregrine was rescued by the island's custodian from rocks at the harbour. The bird was covered in "fulmar oil" and had been in the water where it was mobbed by gulls. It was conveyed by the "Maid of the Forth" to the mainland and taken to S.S.P.C.A. Middlebank Wildlife Centre at Inverkeithing, where it was cleaned and later released.

A male peregrine falcon was flushed from the west cliffs on 24th September the same year.

CORN CRAKE   *Crex crex*

In June 1959 Inchcolm's custodian reported that corn crakes were heard calling from the long grass in two recent summers, before sheep were grazed on the island.

COMMON COOT   *Fulica atra*

A single common coot was seen swimming at Inchcolm's harbour on 13th June 1999 and flew off on the arrival of a boat.

RINGED PLOVER   *Charadrius hiaticula*

On 13th July 1995 two birds were present on the beach at Inchcolm's south bay.

EUROPEAN GOLDEN PLOVER   *Pluvialis apricaria*

Sandeman recorded three birds flying past Carr Craig on 29th July 1948.

PURPLE SANDPIPER   *Calidris maritima*

A single bird was present at Haystack on 24th April 1999.

DUNLIN   *Calidris alpina*

On 11th May 1974 an estimated 250 dunlin were present on Inchcolm. On the same date, between 1,500 - 2,000 dunlin were present on the nearby island of Inchmickery. A large flock of dunlin in summer plumage was seen roosting at Haystack on 21st August 1993.

COMMON SANDPIPER   *Actitis hypoleucos*

One bird was present at Inchcolm on 4th May 1995 and another on 4th July 2002.

WHIMBREL   *Numenius phaeopus*

A whimbrel was recorded at Carr Craig on 29th July 1948, whilst another was seen flying westwards past Haystack on 24th July 1993.

EURASIAN CURLEW   *Numenius arquata*

A number of records exist for eurasian curlew occurring at Inchcolm. The first record is of two birds on 13th July 1954. Single birds were seen on 19th July 1955 and 10th June 1959.

Eurasian curlew were not recorded again until the mid -1990's, although it is certain this species did visit the island during the interim. Single birds were present on 19th July and 19th September 1995, three on 13th November 1996, seventeen on 15th June 1996, two on 18th April 2000 and two on 4th July 2002.

A dead bird, which was the prey of a peregrine, was discovered on 10th November 2001.

RUDDY TURNSTONE   *Arenaria interpres*

Two ruddy turnstone were recorded at Inchcolm on 24th July 1948. The next record is of twenty-five birds occurring on 11th May 1974. Nine further records exist of between one and fifteen birds occurring at the island over the period April 1994 - September 1997.

Three-four ruddy turnstone were recorded at Carr Craig on 1st August 1947. The next record is of eight birds on 25th May 1994. On 25th June 1996 four birds were present. There are seven further records between 29th April 1997 and 30th May 2001 of one - three birds.

POMARINE SKUA   *Stercorarius pomarinus*

A pomarine skua was witnessed chasing a sandwich tern off Inchcolm's north-west cliffs on 19th September 1995. A second bird may have been present on the same date.

ARCTIC SKUA   *Stercorarius parasiticus*

Two birds were recorded from Inchcolm on 26th September 1997, one being a dark-phased bird, the other the light-phased variety.

BLACK-HEADED GULL   *Larus ridibundus*

An immature black-headed gull was recorded from Inchcolm on 13th July 1954. The black-headed gull also featured in a list of birds recorded from the island on 10th July 1955.

There are nine records between June 1994 and September 2002 of between two and ten birds occurring at the island.

Ten birds were at Carr Craig on 25th November 2002.

MEW GULL (Common Gull)   *Larus canus*

Four records exist for the mew gull occurring at Inchcolm. A single bird was present on 13th July 1954, four on 19th July 1955, two on 2nd June 1978 and two - three on 10th February 1998.

COMMON GUILLEMOT   *Uria aalge*

First recorded from Inchcolm on 23rd June 1978, when a single bird was seen flying past the island.

Twelve further records exist for the period June 1993 - November 2002. Most of these records are of one - four individuals swimming close inshore, but occasionally an individual has been seen ashore at Swallowcraig islet, beside the harbour. The most significant record is of five birds swimming singly, close inshore, on 24th September 2002. It is possible the common guillemot may be the next seabird to colonize Inchcolm.

Three records exist for individual birds being close inshore at Haystack: 19th September 1995, 17th June 1997 and 25th November 2002.

Three records also exist for birds being close inshore at Carr Craig: one bird on 29th July 1948, four on 28th May 1996 and another single bird on 24th November 2002.

STOCK PIGEON   *Columba oenas*

One pair of stock pigeons was recorded at Inchcolm on 2nd June 1987.

COMMON CUCKOO   *Cuculus canorus*

Inchcolm's custodian reported a common cuckoo had visited the island for several days during mid - May 1999 and was regularly heard calling.

COMMON SWIFT   *Apus apus*

Four records exist for the common swift occurring at Inchcolm, all of birds flying over the island. Single birds were noted on 24th July 1948, 10th June 1959 and 7th June 1997 and between six - eight birds were seen on 13th July 1954.

GREAT SPOTTED WOODPECKER   *Dendrocopos major*

Inchcolm's custodian reported that a great spotted woodpecker visited the trees in the grounds of the Abbey during early May 1987.

HOUSE MARTIN   *Delichon urbica*

A single house martin flew westwards over the western part of Inchcolm, on 29th May 2001.

NORTHERN WHEATEAR   *Oenanthe oenanthe*

Inchcolm's custodian in 1987, reported the northern wheatear occurred on "passage."

However, the only record since is of a female bird frequenting the Abbey area on 4th May 1995.

FIELDFARE   *Turdus pilaris*

Two records exist for Inchcolm. The island's custodian in 1987 reported the fieldfare occurred at the island on passage and, the custodian in 2002 reported seeing at male bird in the vicinity of the Abbey on 30th June that year.

REDWING   *Turdus illiacus*

As with the fieldfare, Inchcolm's custodian in 1987 reported that this species occurred on passage.

WILLOW WARBLER   *Phylloscopus trochilus*

The willow warbler was first recorded from Inchcolm on 24th July 1948, when a single bird was present. There have been five further records occurring between August 1993 - May 1998, four of them involving single birds and one of two - four birds being present.

BLUE TIT   *Parus caeruleus*

Three records exist for blue tit at Inchcolm. Two birds were present on 13th November 1996, one on 24th April 1999 and at least one on 24th April 2002.

ROOK   *Corvus frugilegus*

Only one record exists for the rook at Inchcolm which is of a single bird flying over the island on 21st April 1994.

EUROPEAN GREENFINCH   *Carduelis chloris*

Four records exist for the european greenfinch occurring at Inchcolm: one bird was singing on 15th July 1950, two - three birds on 13th July 1954, a single bird on 10th June 1959 and a pair on 1st June 1995.

COMMON BULLFINCH   *Pyrrhula pyrrhula*

Inchcolm's custodian reported that a single bullfinch had visited the island at the end of May 1998.

CHILEAN FLAMINGO   *Phoenicopterus chilensis*

In July 1985 a chilean flamingo was observed flying westwards off the north side of Carr Craig towards Inchcolm. This bird is almost certainly the same escapee which was frequenting Loch Leven at that time.

Mammals

From at least the 12th century until the 1980's, domestic animals such as cattle, sheep, pigs and goats have all been kept on Inchcolm at sundry times to satisfy the needs of the various human inhabitants. Rabbits too, were no doubt kept by the monks at the Abbey as a source of food, which probably led to their escape and colonization of the island in past times.

Other than domestic animals, seven species of mammal (if we include the rabbit), have been recorded at, or from, Inchcolm in a live state. They are, the grey and common seal, black rat, otter, american mink, rabbit and bottle-nosed dolphin.

The rabbit is currently extinct and both the otter and american mink have been extremely rare visitors, leaving the black rat as the island's only terrestrial mammal.

Also included are a further two mammal species and one amphibian, merely on account of their remains having been found at Inchcolm (brown hare and common toad) and Carr Craig (common porpoise). In the cases of the brown hare and common toad, their remains were brought to the island by gulls and the common porpoise occurrences appear to have been as a result of strandings.

Usually the only mammals a visitor will encounter at Inchcolm are the grey seal and, less frequently, its smaller cousin the common seal. At the present time there are no domestic stock on the island.

ATLANTIC GREY SEAL   *Halychoerus grypus*

There do not appear to be any old references relating specifically to either the common or the grey seal, occurring at Inchcolm.

During the latter part of the 19th century the grey seal was rare, if not extinct, in the Firth of Forth.

Baxter and Rintoul (Vertebrate Fauna of Forth, 1935) also make no mention of the grey seal having a presence at Inchcolm. It appears that in their time, the grey seal was still uncommon and largely confined to the seaward reaches of the estuary.

The first specific record of the grey seal at Inchcolm is from 23rd June 1976, when about twenty-five seals were present. Most of these were identified as grey seals, with the remainder not being identified at species level.

Since that time the grey seal has been regularly recorded at the island. On most days at least two or three are present about the island's shores, especially at low tide when they will haul themselves out onto the exposed rocks. Up to a dozen or so animals are quite commonplace, but as the 1976 account indicates more than twenty may be found. On 3rd June 2002 twenty-six grey seals were present and on 24th September the same year there were at least twenty-two.

During the 1980's grey seal pups were occasionally born at Inchcolm. The island's custodian reported that in 1993, prior to his vacating the island on 25th October, four grey seal pups had been born.

As a result of this information a visit was made to Inchcolm on 31st October 1994, but no seal pups were found at that time. However, two recently born grey seal pups were discovered on 19th November, one of which was dead.

Only one pup was found during a visit on 13th November 1996, but on 10th November 2001 four pups were discovered. A visit on 25th November 2002 found eleven pups in south bay, all of which were at least two weeks old. Seventeen adult grey seals were also recorded around the island, comprising three bulls and fourteen cows.

At low tide Haystack tends to be a more favoured hauling out place for the grey seal than Inchcolm. However, records of their numbers have only been kept since 1993. On 28th May that year twenty-seven animals were present.

Usually between six - twenty grey seals are found at this rock, but more significant numbers are quite common, e.g. thirty-three on 30th May 2001 and about forty on 30th May 2002.

Small numbers of the grey seal were noted as being present at Carr Craig in July 1985. The next notification we have for this location is of three animals being present on 4th May 1995. Over twenty were recorded on 13th July, that year. Since then up to ten animals have occasionally been noted at this rock.

On 10th November 2001 two recently born pups were observed on the rock from the survey boat. However, no pups were seen during a similar trip on 25th November 2002.

COMMON or HARBOUR SEAL   *Phoca vitulina*

The common seal is believed to have a long established presence in the estuary and it may be that most of the past references actually refer to this species.

In the 12th Century King David I granted a charter to the Monastery at Dunfermline sanctioning them every seventh seal caught at Kinghorn after his own tithe had been set aside. Although not specifically mentioned, it is likely this reference related to the common seal.

Dr. Sibbald (1710) tells us the common seal frequented the Firth of Forth and the isles, in his time, but did not elaborate on which islands.

Our first specific notification of the common seal being identified with the Inchcolm area, is from Baxter and Rintoul (Vertebrate Fauna of Forth, 1935) who stated the common seal had continued to be common up until their time and, that it appeared plentiful on the north side of the Firth between Aberdour and North Queensferry.

On 23rd June 1976 about twenty-five "seals" were recorded at Inchcolm, but most of these were identified as grey seals. Although the common seal was not specifically identified on that occasion, it may have been present.

The common seal occurred regularly at Inchcolm during the 1980's and occasionally the island's Custodian discovered a recently born pup during the summer months over this period.

On 19th September 1995 over fourteen common seals were present on the rocks at the island's north-west bay. During 1997 six were recorded on 17th June, three adults and a very small pup were ashore on 8th July and on 23rd and 26th September twelve animals were ashore.

Since then the common seal has been seen at Inchcolm less frequently and in fewer numbers. In 1998 two were present on 23rd March, four on 13th May and two again on 11th June. One animal was ashore on 13th June 1999 and another on 18th April 2000.

Small numbers of common seal have occasionally been seen at Carr Craig since 1994, usually involving one-two animals. However, three were ashore on 13th July 1995 and four likewise on 31st May 2002.

So far the common seal has only been recorded once at Haystack. Three were observed hauled out at the rock on 6th July 1993.

There is little doubt that the occurrence of the common seal at Inchcolm and Carr Craig has been a lot more frequent than records indicate.

BOTTLE-NOSED DOLPHIN   *Tursiops truncatus*

During 1996 and 1997 a single bottle-nosed dolphin frequented the inner Forth estuary and was most often found swimming between the Forth Rail Bridge and Inchcolm. It was frequently seen by passengers board the "Maid of the Forth" as the vessel plied between South Queensferry and the island and made a habit of escorting boats as they journeyed up and down the firth.

On 15th June 1996 the dolphin was seen leaping out of the water several times between Haystack and Braefoot terminal on the Fife shore and on 13th November that year it was recorded off the north side of Inchcolm, where it remained for quite some time.

The dolphin was again recorded off Haystack on 24th May 1997. Later that day it was seen leaping out of the water, close inshore at the east end of Inchcolm. It re-visited this location again on 27th May.

COMMON or HARBOUR PORPOISE   *Phocoena phocoena*

On 3rd June 1996 two skeletons of a mammal (each 3 - 4' in length), believed to be of this species, were discovered on the west shore of Carr Craig. They were lying close together and may have become stranded at the rock and subsequently died. In July 1985 a single skeleton of what is believed to be the same species, was also found at the same location.

The common porpoise is a regular feature in the Firth of Forth, but can be very difficult to see unless it is a very calm day.

BROWN HARE   *Lepus europaeus*

The brown hare has only been included by virtue of a pair of hare's ears which were found on the western part of Inchcolm, on 17th June 1997. These were discovered lying in the gull colony and could only have been brought to the island by a gull, following a visit to the mainland.

RABBIT   *Oryctolagus cuniculus*

One old reference from the 16th century states the islands in the Forth were "verie full of conies (rabbits)" and presumably this included Inchcolm. A further reference from 1547 mentions "cooniges" as inhabiting "Sainct Coomes Ins" (Inchcolm).

Dr. Sibbald in his "History of Fife and Kinross" (1710) also stated there were conies on Inchcolm, and Dickson (Emeralds Chased in Gold, 1899) stated that rabbits breed plentifully at the island.

It is likely that rabbits were introduced to Inchcolm by the Augustinian monks from the Abbey as a source of food and revenue at some point between the 13th and 16th centuries.

According to Baxter and Rintoul (Vertebrate Fauna of Forth, 1935), rabbits still inhabited Inchcolm in their day.

Despite the rabbit having been present on Inchcolm for centuries, it is not found there today. It appears they disappeared from the island near the middle of the 20th Century, possibly due to the large scale build up of military works at Inchcolm during the Second World War, or, the Ministry of Works, owners of the island at that time, exterminated the rabbits at some time after the war as part of their attempts to restore the Abbey and its grounds to a public amenity.

BLACK RAT   *Rattus rattus*

Inchcolm has a substantial black rat population, judging by the accounts of some who have lived and worked on the island. However, this species is rarely seen by visiting members of the public due to its largely secretive and nocturnal habits.

During the 1980's and again in the late1990's, corpses of "rats" were removed from the island and scientifically identified as the black rat. To date there is no record of the brown rat ever having occurred at Inchcolm.

Just when the black rat first appeared at Inchcolm is unknown. However, it is likely that it was well established before its presence was discovered.

During the various outbreaks of the great plague (bubonic plague), i.e. 15th-17th centuries, some ships arriving at the Firth of Forth with outbreaks of the plague on board, were ordered to anchor off either Inchkeith or Inchcolm, where the sick were quarantined until they either died or recovered and the ships' cargoes were unloaded and aired in the sun to try and combat the pestilence.

At that time it was unknown that the plague was transmitted by infected fleas carried by the black rat, finding their way onto human beings and feeding on their blood, thereby infecting their new hosts with the disease.

In this scenario it is easy to see how the black rat could have had opportunity to colonize Inchcolm. It is possible they also did so on Inchkeith, but were later replaced by the brown rat on that island. However, Dickson (Emeralds Chased in Gold, 1899) stated that "rabbits breed plentifully at Inchcolm, but there are no rats"

Although the absence of records indicating the presence of rats at Inchcolm prior to Dickson's time, does not necessarily endorse a rat - free status for the past, some cognizance has to be given to his statement. This would mean that today's population of black rats, have descended from pioneers arriving at the island at some point during the 20th century.

The black rat was recorded from Inchcolm on 23rd June 1976 when the island's Custodian reported it as being "numerous" and that "many were poisoned or trapped". The fact this species was causing such a problem to those residing on the island, suggests its presence was well known before this time.

A later Custodian also reported the black rat as being numerous in June 1987 and also that it was poisoned and trapped, in an effort to control its numbers.

Up to the present time those living on the island, or involved in maintenance work at the island's buildings, have regularly reported seeing either the black rat itself, or evidence of its presence.

It is possible the black rat could have received "assisted passage" from any sizeable boat calling at the island during the early - mid 20th century, but the likeliest periods for its introduction are during the First and Second World War periods, when the island was heavily built up with military defences, associated buildings and personnel.

The presence of the black rat should not deter any potential visitors from making a trip to Inchcolm, as in over one hundred visits to this beautiful island, the author has only once seen a live black rat (11th June 1998) and only for a brief moment at that.

Interestingly, the black rat is now considered something of an endangered species. Being the first of the two rat species to colonize the British Isles over eight centuries ago it soon became widespread, but since the arrival of the larger brown rat in the 18th century it has become displaced from most of its habitat and as far as is known, is now restricted to only three locations, all of which are islands: Inchcolm in the Firth of Forth, North Rona in the Outer Hebrides and Lundy in the Bristol Channel.

Inchcolm, therefore, may be regarded as a sanctuary for this dwindling species.

AMERICAN MINK   *Mustela vison*

Maintenance staff from Historic Scotland apparently saw single mink at Inchcolm on two occasions, a year or two apart, during the late 1990's. Unfortunately more precise information is unknown. These animals undoubtedly made their way to the island from the Fife mainland.

OTTER *Lutra lutra*

Dr. Sibbald in his "History of Fife and Kinross" (1710) stated "the sea otter lives in the coves upon the Fife coast, and in the isles." He mistakenly credits this animal (in this country) as being a distinctly separate species from the common otter. Nevertheless, the indication remains that in Dr. Sibbald's time otters were known to visit the islands in the Firth of Forth. However, Dr. Sibbald does not specifically mention any island by name, but with Inchcolm being one of those islands which are closest to the mainland, it is likely he had this island in mind.

On 2nd February 1994 maintenance staff from Historic Scotland saw an otter run from a large hole near the harbour and enter the sea.

About this time otters were being reported from the Aberdour area and it would be no problem for an adventurous otter to swim out to Inchcolm, especially at low tide when there are exposed rocks lying between the mainland and the island.

NORTHERN FULMAR CHICK

AMPHIBIA

COMMON TOAD   *Bufo bufo*

A complete, but dried out corpse of a common toad, was found lying in the gull colony at the western part of Inchcolm on 26th June 1995 and could only have been brought to the island by a gull, following a visit to the mainland.

HERRING AND LESSER BLACK-BACKED GULLS

BUTTERFLIES

The following list of butterflies recorded at Inchcolm has been compiled from occasional sightings made by R.A.Morris during visits to the island, mainly from 1994 onwards. These records are, in the main, casual observations made during the course of monitoring breeding seabird numbers. So far nine species of butterfly have been recorded. The island's moth population has still to receive attention, but Morris noted the six-spot burnet moth (*Zygaena filipendulae*) during the mid -1980's. This species has not been recorded from the island since that time.

Pieridae

LARGE WHITE   *Pieris brassicae*
Recorded in June and September 1995, May, June and July 1997 and June 1999.
SMALL WHITE   *Artogeia rapae*
Recorded in May, June and July 1995, April, May, June and July 1997 and April and July 1999.
GREEN-VEINED WHITE   *Artogeia napi*
Recorded in June 1994, July 1995, April, May, and July 1997 and July 1999.

Satyridae

MEADOW BROWN   *Maniola jurtina*
Recorded during the mid 1980's, June, July and August 1994, July 1995, July 1997 and July 1999.

Nymphalidae

SMALL TORTOISESHELL   *Aglais urticae*
Recorded in August 1994, May and July 1995, May 1996, April, May and June 1997, April and July 1999 and September 2002.
RED ADMIRAL   *Vanessa atalanta*
Recorded in July 1994, July and September 1995, May, June and July 1997, April, July and August 1999 and September 2002.
PAINTED LADY   *Vanessa cardui*
Recorded in July 1996 and September 2002.
PEACOCK   *Inachis io*
Recorded in September 2002.

Lycaenidae

COMMON BLUE   *Polyommatus icarus*
Recorded during the mid 1980's, but not since.

FLORA

Apart from the grounds of the Abbey and tourist reception area, Inchcolm is largely dominated by coastal grassland vegetation, with an increasing amount of Elder which is now found throughout the island. There are also attractive thickets of Sea Buckthorn and Snowberry at the island's east part and some tall examples of Sycamore and Ash grow in the vicinity of the Custodian's house, west of the Abbey.

History shows us that Inchcolm's few acres have long attracted the activities of man, some of which, due to being minor in nature, would have had little impact on the island's vegetation, but other activities, which were quite extensive enterprises, would certainly have had considerable influence in shaping its character.

As early as 1123 a lone Hermit stayed on the island, surviving on what humble fare Inchcolm's shores would provide. During that year, Alexander I and his entourage were driven onto the island by a storm whilst crossing the Forth and were sustained by the Hermit for several days on the milk from a single cow and shellfish gathered from the shore.

Alexander had made a vow during the stormy crossing, that he would found a Monastery on the island of Aemonia (as Inchcolm was then called) if his life was spared. Unfortunately he died the following year before he could fulfill his promise, but his brother David I, carried out his wishes and founded a small Monastery in the keep of Augustinian monks.

This establishment grew in size and importance over the next four centuries, eventually reaching the status of Abbey. During this time the community of monks tilled the island's soil, planted crops and maintained domestic stock.

However, at the time of the Reformation in 1560 the Abbey was disbanded and the island appears to have been left to return to the wild for well over two centuries, save for the occasional brief period of occupancy by individuals, a family, or when the island was occasionally just used for grazing.

Dr. Sibbald, visited Inchcolm early in the 18th century and his "History of Fife and Kinross" has left us with the first insight into Inchcolm's botanical history, which is worth repeating in full; "This east part is fit for the pasture of a few sheep. I found the *Verbascum majus*, called commonly the Shepherd's Club, growing upon it. There are several small rocks about this part of the isle, where there is good fishing. The west part of the isle is both longer and broader, the grass is very good in it, and there are many Conies in it: The soil produceth many fine plants, especially on the side which looketh to the north; such as *Cochlearia* or Scurvy-grass, *Folio sinuoso, Isatis sive glastum, Gramen marinum longius, Gr. junceum,* and *Gr. minus tenuissimum.* In the garden adjacent to the monastery, I found the female Paeonie bearing seed, common Borage, and Pellitorie, the dwarf Elder, the *Echium flore albo,* Solanum dictum bella donna, and the *Malva pumula flore albo, Tribus lineis rubris distincto."*

Towards the end of the 18th Century, when the threat of Napoleon hung over our shores, a fort comprising of two batteries was erected on the eastern part of Inchcolm, to resist any attempt at invasion. The batteries were dismantled early in the 19th Century after Napoleon was finally defeated.

Later that century Inchcolm started to develop as the tourist attraction, which it remains today.

John Dickson, writing in his "Emeralds Chased in Gold" (1899), gives us another important account of Inchcolm's botanical assets, which is also worth repeating in full: "Inchcolm is admirably adapted for grazing purposes. Its natural pasturage is rich and well mixed with clover (*Trifolium repens*). Much of the island might be made arable. The soil, in the immediate vicinity of the Monastery, is very fertile, producing excellent crops of potatoes and turnips. Oats formerly used to be grown. The *flora* is exceedingly varied and similar to that of the mainland. Shrubs are rare with the exception of the Elder-berry (*Sambucus nigra*), which is plentiful around the Monastery; and the Wild-rose (*Rosa canina*) on the west side of the island. There are also a few Plane, Ash, and Laburnum trees; but they are of a somewhat stunted growth. Ferns are scarce, although a few species, including the common bracken, may be picked up here and there. Poppies of various hues, grow in great abundance; but the familiar red poppy (*Papaver rhoaeus*) is by no means rife. There is a considerable variety of other wild flowers among which may be mentioned, the Buttercup (*Ranunculus*); Biting Stone-crop (*Sedum acre*); Common-yarrow (*Achillea millefolium*); Groundsel (*Senecio vulgaris*); Wild Thyme (*Thymus serpyllum*); Bird's-foot Trefoil (*Lotus corniculatus*); Speedwell (*Veronica serpyllifolia*); Thrift or sea-pink; Vetch (*Vetch sativa*); and Wood sorrel (*Oxalis acetosella*)."

With regard to Dickson's account, the Plane (i.e. Sycamore) and Ash trees referred to as, "of a somewhat stunted growth," have since grown into large examples of their kind. Due to the type of habitat at Inchcolm it is believed that *Papaver rhoaeus* (Corn Poppy) and *Oxalis acetosella* (Wood Sorrel) may have been misidentified and were more likely to have been *Papaver dubium*, (Long-headed Poppy) and *Rumex acetosa* (Common Sorrel) respectively. Also *Vetch sativa* appears to be a misprint and should read *Victa sativa*.

Inchcolm's attraction as a tourist amenity was interrupted for the periods of both the World Wars of the 20th Century, when the island was heavily built up and its soil displaced on an unprecedented scale to allow for the construction of gun batteries, ammunition stores, engine houses, hutted encampments, trenches, etc, which on both occasions virtually covered the island, especially so during the second conflict.

For such a small place, provided with a generally thin covering of soil, these activities must have had a major impact on the character of the island's vegetation. Several years after each war most of the military buildings and fortifications were removed in an attempt to return the island to its former amenity. However, a substantial proportion of the military works still remain.

For decades the attractive gardens within the grounds of the Abbey, which contain many introduced plant species, have been maintained by Inchcolm's successive Custodians and other staff employed by Historic Scotland.

Sheep were last grazed on the island's western pastures during the early 1980's. Since then most of the island has been left to its own devices and the vegetation once more has been left to the wild course of nature.

The gull colonies, which now carpet most of the wild parts of the island during the spring and summer months, undoubtedly have had their own influence on the island's vegetation with their dunging and nest-building habits, displacing some plant species whilst allowing others to proliferate. However, their influence so far is not nearly as pronounced as on Inchkeith, which is a much more exposed and hillier island.

A number of attempts have taken place in recent times to interpret Inchcolm's undoubted wealth of flora. In June 1966 Elizabeth P. Beattie visited the island in connection with her studies of flora on all the islands in the Firth of Forth. Her findings are listed in the Transactions of the Botanical Society of Edinburgh (Vol. 40, 1967, pages 251-257). Due to her limited time ashore at each of the islands her lists can hardly be expected to be complete, although they are extensive and have provided a sound foundation for future efforts.

Douglas MacKean from the Royal Botanic Garden, Edinburgh, visited Inchcolm in June and August 1994 for the purpose of expanding on Beattie's lists, and George Ballantyne (Fife's Botanical Recorder) also visited the island in August that year for the purpose of obtaining botanical information.

In August 1999 Louise Allen, on behalf of the Scottish Wildlife Trust, visited the island on two occasions in order to carry out a further botanical survey.

In preparation for this booklet, George Ballantyne has collated all the information from the aforementioned surveys, as well as a number of important records from the past and assembled them into the following comprehensive list of flowering plants recorded from Inchcolm. Undoubtedly there are other plant species on the island that have yet to be identified, including of course, the lower plants such as mosses and lichens.

Family and Botanical Name	Common Name
Pteropsida	
Asplenium adiantum-nigrum	Black Spleenwort
Asplenium marinum	Sea Spleenwort
Asplenium ruta-muraria	Wall Rue
Dryopteris dilatata	Broad Buckler Fern
Dryopteris filix-mas	Male Fern
Phyllitis scolopendrium	Hart's-tongue
Polypodium interjectum	Intermediate Polypody
Ranunculaceae	
Ranunculus acris	Meadow Buttercup
Ranunculus repens	Creeping Buttercup
Papaveraceae	
Papaver dubium	Long-headed Poppy
Papaver somniferum	Opium Poppy
Brassicaceae (Cruciferae)	
Arabidopsis thaliana	Thale Cress
Aubrieta deltoidea	Aubretia
Brassica napus	Rape
Brassica oleracea	Wild Cabbage
Brassica rapa	Wild Turnip
Cakile maritima	Sea Rocket
Capsella bursa-pastoris	Shepherd's Purse
Cardamine hirsuta	Hairy Bitter-cress
Cochlearia danica	Danish Scurvy-grass
Cochlearia officinalis	Common Scurvy-grass
Crambe maritima	Sea Kale
Erysimum cheiri	Wallflower
Erophila verna	Whitlow Grass
Iberis amara	Candytuft
Isatis tinctoria	Woad
Sinapis arvensis	Charlock

Family and Botanical Name	Common Name
Sisymbrium officinale	Hedge Mustard
Sisymbrium orientale	Eastern Rocket
Thlaspi arvense	Field Penny Cress
Resedaceae	
Reseda luteola	Weld
Violoceae	
Viola arvensis	Field Pansy
Viola riviniana	Dog Violet
Carophyllaceae	
Arenaria serpyllifolia	Thyme-leaved Sandwort
Cerastium diffusum	Sea Mouse-ear
Cerastium fontanum	Common Mouse-ear
Cerastium semidecandrum	Little Mouse-ear
Cerastium tomentosum	Snow-in-summer
Dianthus caryophyllus	Clove Pink
Honckenya peploides	Sea Sandwort
Moehringia trinervia	Three-nerved Sandwort
Sagina apetala	Annual Pearlwort
Sagina maritima	Sea Pearlwort
Sagina procumbens	Procumbent Pearlwort
Silene latifolia	White Campion
Silene uniflora	Sea Campion
Stellaria media	Common Chickweed
Chenopodiaceae	
Atriplex glabriuscula	Babington's Orache
Atriplex laciniata	Frosted Orache
Atriplex littoralis	Grass-leaved Orache
Atriplex prostrata	Spear-leaved Orache
Beta maritima	Sea-beet
Salsola kali	Prickly Saltwort
Euphorbiaceae	
Euphorbia peplus	Petty Spurge

Family and Botanical Name	Common Name
Malvaceae	
Lavatera arborea	Tree Mallow
Malva sylvestris	Common Mallow
Linaceae	
Linum catharticum	Fairy Flax
Geraniaceae	
Erodium cicutarium	Common Stork's-bill
Geranium molle	Dove's-foot Crane's-bill
Geranium pratense	Meadow Crane's-bill
Geranium pyrenaicum	Hedgerow Crane's-bill
Aceraceae	
Acer pseudoplatanus	Sycamore
Papilionaceae	
Anthyllis vulneraria	Kidney-vetch
Cytisus scoparius	Broom
Laburnum anagyroides	Laburnum
Lathyrus pratensis	Meadow Vetchling
Lotus corniculatus	Common Bird's-foot Trefoil
Medicago lupulina	Black Medick
Trifolium arvense	Hare's-foot Clover
Trifolium campestre	Hop Trefoil
Trifolium dubium	Lesser Trefoil
Trifolium pratense	Red Clover
Trifolium repens	White Clover
Ulex europaeus	Whin
Vicia cracca	Tufted Vetch
Vicia hirsuta	Hairy Tare
Vicia sativa (sub-species "nigra")	Narrow-leaved Vetch
Vicia sepium	Bush Vetch
Rosaceae	
Agrimonia eupatoria	Agrimony

Family and Botanical Name	Common Name
Cotoneaster horizontalis	Wallspray
Malus domestica	Apple
Potentilla anserina	Silverweed
Rosa canina	Common Dog Rose
Rubus idaeus	Raspberry
Rubus latifolius	Bramble
Rubus radula	Bramble
Sorbus aucuparia	Rowan
Crassulaceae	
Sedum acre	Biting Stonecrop
Grossulariaceae	
Ribes sanguineus	Flowering Currant
Ribes uva-crispa	Gooseberry
Elaeagnaceae	
Hippophae rhamnoides	Sea Buckthorn
Ulmaceae	
Ulmus glabra	Wych Elm
Onagraceae	
Chamerion angustifolium	Rosebay Willowherb
Epilobium ciliatum	American Willowherb
Epilobium montanum	Broad-leaved Willowherb
Apiaceae (Umbelliferae)	
Aegopodium millefolium	Bishopweed
Anthriscus caucalis	Bur Chervil
Conium maculatum	Hemlock
Conopodium majus	Pignut
Daucus carota	Wild Carrot
Heracleum sphondylium	Hogweed
Ligusticum scoticum	Scots' Lovage
Torilis japonica	Upright Hedge Parsley
Araliaceae	
Hedera helix	Ivy

Family and Botanical Name	Common Name
Polygonaceae	
Polygonum aviculare	Knot Grass
Rumex acetosa	Common Sorrel
Rumex acetosella	Sheep's Sorrel
Rumex crispus	Curled Dock
Rumex obtusifilius	Broad-leaved Dock
Urticaceae	
Parietaria judaica	Pellitory-of-the-Wall
Urtica dioica	Common Nettle
Urtica urens	Small Nettle
Plumbaginaceae	
Armeria maritima	Thrift; Sea Pink
Oleaceae	
Fraxinus excelsior	Ash
Ligustrum ovalifolium	Garden Privet
Boraginaceae	
Anchusa arvensis	Lesser Bugloss
Asperugo procumbens	Madwort
Borago officinalis	Borage
Cynoglossum officinale	Hound's-tongue
Echium vulgare	Viper's Bugloss
Myosotis arvensis	Field Forget-me-not
Pentaglottis sempervirens	Green Alkanet
Solanaceae	
Atropa belladonna	Deadly Nightshade
Hyoscyamus niger	Henbane
Lycium chinense	Chinese Teaplant
Solanum dulcamara	Bittersweet
Scrophulariaceae	
Cymbalaria muralis	Ivy-leaved Toadflax
Euphrasia arctica	Eyebright
Linaria vulgaris	Common Toadflax

Family and Botanical Name	Common Name
Odontites vernus	Red Bartsia
Scrophularia nodosa	Common Figwort
Verbascum thapsus	Common Mullein
Veronica arvensis	Wall Speedwell
Veronica chamaedrys	Germander Speedwell
Veronica serpyllifolia	Thyme-leaved Speedwell
Lamiaceae (Labiatae)	
Galeopsis tetrahit	Common Hemp-nettle
Glechoma hederacea	Ground Ivy
Lamium purpureum	Red Dead-nettle
Marrubium vulgare	Common Horehound
Mentha x piperita	Peppermint
Prunella vulgaris	Selfheal
Teucrium scorodonia	Wood Sage
Thymus polytrichus	Wild Thyme
Plantaginaceae	
Plantago coronopus	Buck's-horn Plantain
Plantago lanceolata	Ribwort Plantain
Plantago major	Greater Plantain
Plantago maritima	Sea Plantain
Campanulaceae	
Campanula rotundifolia	Harebell (Scottish Bluebell)
Rubiaceae	
Galium aparine	Stickie Willie
Galium verum	Lady's Bedstraw
Sherardia arvensis	Field Madder
Dipsacaceae	
Dipsacus fullonum	Wild Teasel
Caprifoliaceae	
Lonicera periclymenum	Honeysuckle
Sambucus ebulus	Dwarf Elder
Sambucus nigra	Elder
Symphoricarpos albus	Snowberry

Family and Botanical Name	Common Name

Compositae

Achillea millefolium	Yarrow
Artemisia absinthium	Wormwood
Bellis perennis	Daisy
Carduus crispus	Welted Thistle
Carduus tenuiflorus	Slender Thistle
Centaurea nigra	Common Knapweed
Cichorium intybus	Chicory
Cirsium arvense	Creeping Thistle
Cirsium palustre	Marsh Thistle
Cirsium vulgare	Spear Thistle
Crepis capillaris	Smooth Hawk`s-beard
Hypochaeris radicata	Cat`s Ear
Lapsana communis	Nipplewort
Leucanthemum vulgare	Ox-eye Daisy
Matricaria discoidea	Pineapple Weed
Pilosella officinarum	Mouse-ear Hawkweed
Senecio jacobaea	Common Ragwort
Senecio sylvaticus	Heath Groundsel
Senecio viscosus	Sticky Groundsel
Senecio vulgaris	Groundsel
Sonchus arvensis	Perennial Sow-thistle
Sonchus asper	Prickly Sow-thistle
Sonchus oleraceus	Smooth Sow-thistle
Taraxacum officinale	Dandelion
Tragopogon pratensis	Goat`s-beard
Tripleurospermum inodorum	Scentless Mayweed
Tripleurospermum maritimum	Sea Mayweed

Primulaceae

Anagallis arvensis	Scarlet Pimpernel

Liliaceae

Hyacinthoides non-scriptus	Wild Hyacinth

Family and Botanical Name	Common Name
Cyperaceae	
Carex muricata	Prickly Sedge
Carex otrubae	False Fox Sedge
Poaceae (Gramineae)	
Agrostis capillaris	Common Bent-grass
Agrostis stolonifera	Fiorin
Aira caryophyllea	Silvery Hair-grass
Aira praecox	Early Hair-grass
Alopecurus pratensis	Meadow Foxtail
Ammophila arenaria	Marram
Anisantha sterilis	Barren Brome
Anthoxanthum adoratum	Sweet Vernal-grass
Arrhenatherum elatius	False Oat-grass
Avena fatua	Wild Oat
Brachypodium sylvaticum	False Brome
Bromus hordeaceus	Soft Brome
Catapodium rigidum	Fern-grass
Cynosurus cristatus	Crested Dog's-tail
Dactylis glomerata	Cock's-foot
Danthonia decumbens	Heath-grass
Elytrigia junceiforme	Sand Couch
Elytrigia repens	Common Couch
Festuca ovina	Sheep's Fescue
Festuca rubra	Red Fescue
Helictotrichon pratense	Meadow Oat-grass
Holcus lanatus	Yorkshire-fog
Hordeum distichon	Barley
Hordeum murinum	Wall Barley
Koeleria macrantha	Crested Hair-grass
Lolium perenne	Perennial Ryegrass
Phleum arenarium	Sand Cat's-tail
Poa annua	Annual Meadow-grass

Family and Botanical Name	Common Name
Poa pratensis	Smooth Meadow-grass
Poa trivialis	Rough Meadow-grass
Trisetum flavescens	Yellow Oat-grass
Pinaceae	
Pinus sylvestris	Scots Pine

EUROPEAN SHAGS

LIST OF FLORA RECORDED FROM CARR CRAIG & HAYSTACK

Prior to 1951 Carr Craig had had a fairly lush covering of vegetation, until the rock was taken over by nesting gulls, which destroyed all of the rock's flora with their nest building and dunging habits. A similar situation also appears to have been the case with Haystack.

On 5th May, 1995 Douglas MacKean visited both rocks in order to establish their up to date status in respect of plant-life and recorded the following species growing at Carr Craig . He found no plant-life growing at Haystack. However, a single plant record dating from 1710 exists in relation to that rock.

CARR CRAIG

Brassicaceae (Cruciferae)
Capsella bursa-pastoris   Shepherd's Purse
Cochlearia danica   Danish Scurvy-grass
Apiaceae (Umbelliferae)
Conium maculatum   Hemlock
Chenopodiaceae
Atriplex sp.   An Orache
Compositae
Senecio vulgaris   Groundsel
Taraxacum officinale   Dandelion
Tripleurospermum maritimum   Sea Mayweed
Poaceae (Gramineae)
Holcus lanatus   Yorkshire Fog
Poa annua   Annual Meadow-grass
Festuca rubra   Red Fescue

HAYSTACK

Chenopodiaceae
Chenopodium vulvaria   Stinking Goose-foot

NOTES